The Complete Guitar Player James Taylor Songbook

by Arthur Dick.

Wise Publications
London/New York/Sydney

Exclusive Distributors:
Music Sales Limited
8/9 Frith Street, London W1V 5TZ, England.
Music Sales Pty Limited
120 Rothschild Avenue, Rosebery, NSW 2018, Australia.

This book © Copyright 1990 by
Wise Publications
Order No. AM78882
UK ISBN 0.7119.2177.6

Cover design by Pearce Marchbank Studio
Photograph by Pictorial Press
Arranged by Arthur Dick
Compiled by Peter Evans
Music processed by Musicprint

Music Sales' complete catalogue lists thousands of
titles and is free from your local music shop, or direct from
Music Sales Limited. Please send £1 in stamps for postage to
Music Sales Limited, 8/9 Frith Street, London W1V 5TZ.

Printed in the United Kingdom by
J. B. Offset Printers (Marks Tey) Limited, Marks Tey, Essex.

Sweet Baby James
Words & Music by James Taylor

:3/4 Rhythm/Bass & Strum
See Course Book No. 1 Page 17

Count: 1   2 & 3 &

There is a young cow-boy, he lives on the range. ___ His

horse and his cat-tle are his on-ly com-pan-ions; ___ He works in the sad-dle and he sleeps in the can-yons

Wait-ing for sum-mer his pas-tures to change. ___ And as the moon ri-ses he sits by his

fire ___ Think-ing 'bout wo-men and glass-es of beer And clos-ing his eyes as the dog-gies re-tire, He

sings out a song which is soft but it's clear As if may-be some-one could hear.

Good-night, you moon-light lad - ies, ___ Rock-a-bye, sweet Ba-by James. Deep greens and blues are the

col-ours I choose, Won't you let me go down in my dreams, And rock-a-bye, sweet Ba-by James. Now the

Verse 2
Now the first of December was covered in snow
And so was the turnpike from Stockbridge to Boston
The Berkshires seemed dreamlike on account of that frosting
With ten miles behind me and ten thousand more to go.
There's a song that they sing when they take to the highway

A song that they sing when they take to the sea.
A song that they sing of their home in the sky
Maybe you can believe it if it helps you to sleep
But singin' works just fine for me.

Night Owl Words & Music by James Taylor

4/4 Rhythm/Strumming/Lively
See Course Book No. 1 Page 12

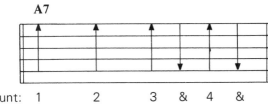

Count: 1   2   3 & 4 &

A cat - fish _ he tends to groove _ on the wa - ter it's just where _ he's bound to be, _

_ And a mon - key kind of flash - es on fruits _ and ba - na - nas so he

lives in the top of a tree, _____ But my eyes are made _ for dark -

- ness _ and so the night-time is right for me _ Said I'm a

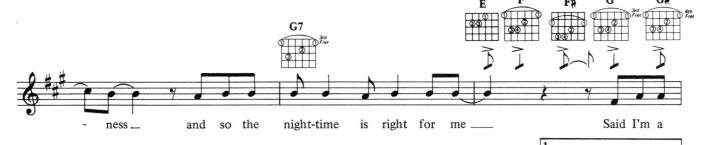

night owl, _ hon - ey, sleep all _ day _ long. Now,

Said, turn off that bright, _ light, ba - by, you're

just a - bout _ to drive me blind, _ Draw them cur - tains for me, ma -

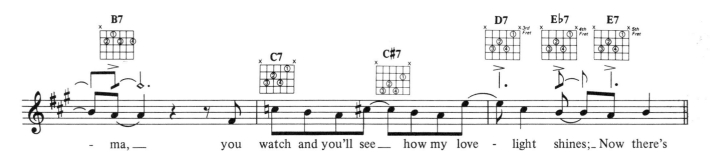

- ma, ___ you watch and you'll see ___ how my love - light shines; _ Now there's

two sides to this great __ big world __ and one of them is al - ways night, __ Hey, _ if you can

take care of bus - 'ness in the sun - shine, ba - by, __ I guess you're goin' to be all right, __

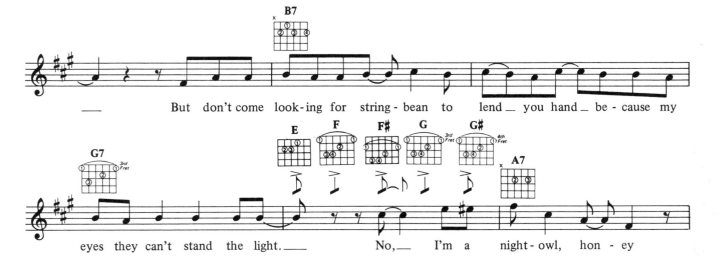

__ But don't come look-ing for string - bean to lend __ you hand __ be - cause my

eyes they can't stand the light. __ No, __ I'm a night - owl, hon - ey

sleep all _ sleep _ all __ day _ long I said, sleep all __ day _ long. _

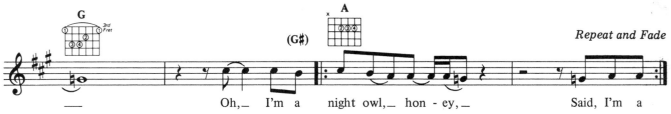

Repeat and Fade

(G#)

Oh, _ I'm a night owl, _ hon - ey, _ Said, I'm a

Verse 2
Now most folks like the good daytime,
Baby, they like to see the shining sun,
They're up in the morning off and running
'Til they're too tired for having fun.
But when the sun goes down and the bright lights shine
My daytime has just begun.

Chorus
Woh, I'm a night owl honey
Woh, sleep all day long —

5

Song For You Far Away
Words & Music by James Taylor

4/4 Rhythm/Simple arpeggio with moving bass line
See Course Book No. 1 Page 27

CAPO 1st FRET

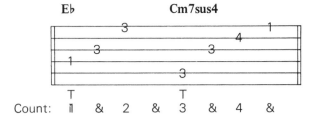

Count: 1 & 2 & 3 & 4 &

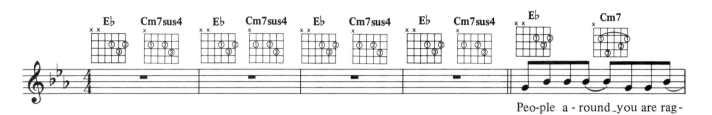

Peo-ple a - round_you are rag-

- ged a - gain._ God on-ly knows how they do ___ it. One to an-oth - er, then

back a - gain. Some-thing keeps put-ting them through it. Me, I've been watch-ing more than

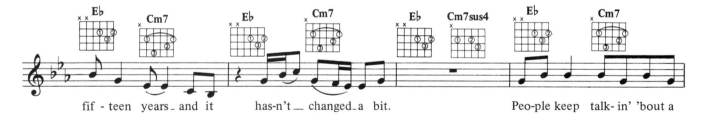

fif - teen years_ and it has-n't _ changed_a bit. Peo-ple keep talk-in' 'bout a

CHORUS

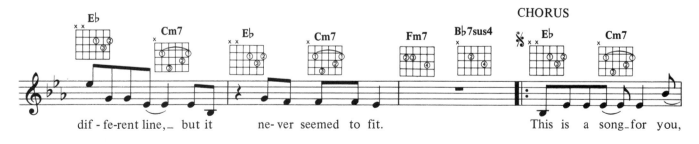

dif - fe-rent line,_ but it ne - ver seemed to fit. This is a song_for you,

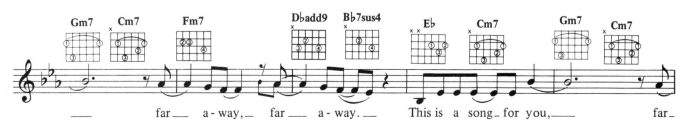

___ far - a-way,_ far ___ a-way. This is a song_ for you,___ far _

Repeat Chorus
This is a song for you
Far away, so far away
This is a song for you
Far away from me.

Rainy Day Man

Words & Music by James Taylor

4/4 Rhythm/Ballad Strum
See Course Book No. 1 Page 14

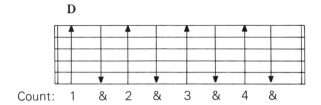

What good is __ that hap- py lie? ___ All you want-ed from the start __ was to cry, ___ girl. It looks like an-oth-er fall, ___ your friends they don't seem to help at all. ___ Now when you're feel-ing kind of cold and small ___ Just look up your rain-y day man. ___ It does you no good __ to pre-tend, ___ you've made a hole much too big __ to mend ___ And it looks like you lose __ a-gain, my friend. ___ So go on home and look up your rain-y day man. ___ Now

rain-y day __ man don't ___ like sun-shine, __ he don't chase no rain-bows, he
sim-ple plea-sures, they all ___ e-vade you, __ store bought trea-sures, ___ Lord,

Anywhere Like Heaven
Words & Music by James Taylor

4/4 Rhythm/Bass-strum
See Course Book No. 1 Page 18

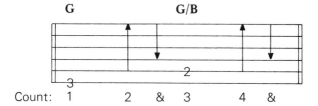

Count: 1   2   &   3   4   &

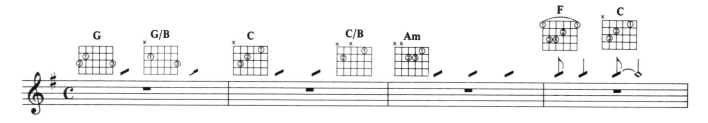

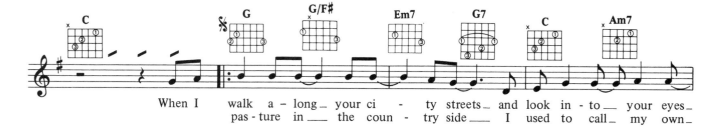

When I walk a-long your ci - ty streets and look in - to your eyes
pas - ture in the coun - try side I used to call my own

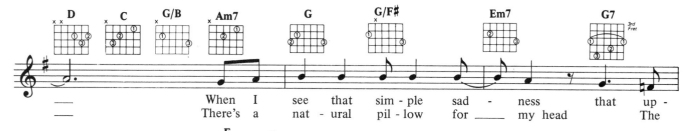

When I see that sim - ple sad - ness that up-
There's a nat - ural pil - low for my head The

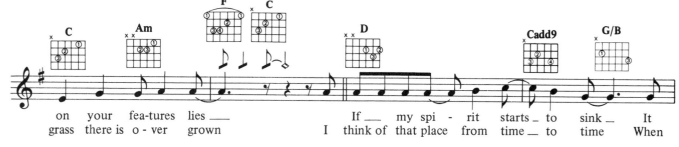

on your fea - tures lies If my spi - rit starts to sink It
grass there is o - ver grown I think of that place from time to time When

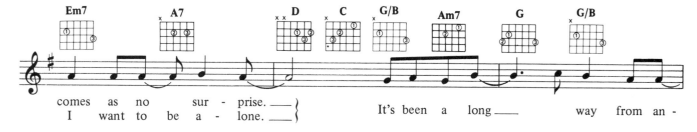

comes as no sur - prise. ┘ It's been a long way from an -
I want to be a - lone. ┘

1.

Fine

N.C.

- y - where Like hea - ven to your town, this town. There's a

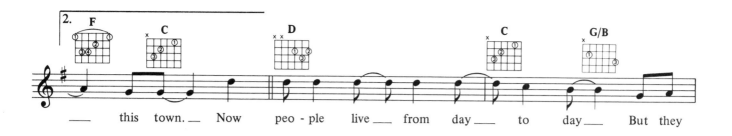

this town.__ Now peo-ple live __ from day __ to day __ But they

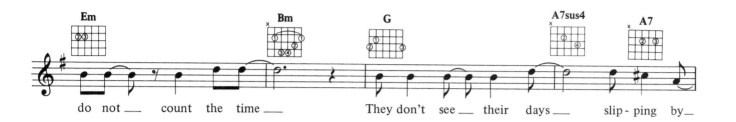

do not __ count the time __ They don't see __ their days __ slip-ping by __

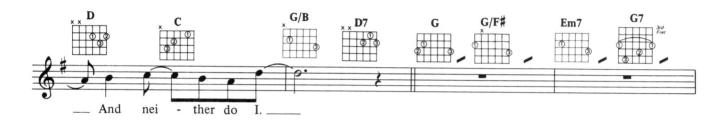

__ And nei - ther do I. _____

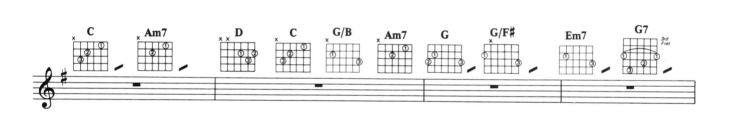

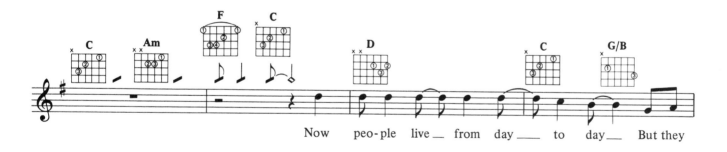

Now peo-ple live __ from day __ to day __ But they

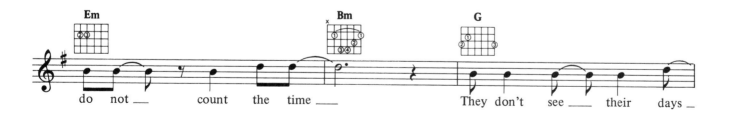

do not __ count the time __ They don't see __ their days __

D.S. al Fine

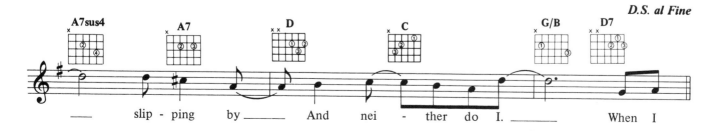

__ slip - ping by _____ And nei - ther do I. _____ When I

Carolina In My Mind

Words & Music by James Taylor

4/4 Rhythm/Bass-strum
See Course Book No. 1 Pages 18-22

thing soft — and kind.   And hey, babe, the sky's on fire, I'm dy - ing, ain't I?   I'm

D.%. al Coda   ⊕ *CODA*

gone to Ca - ro - li - na - in — my mind. _____   _____   Now with a

ho - ly host of oth-ers stand - ing 'round — me — no, _____   Still I'm on — the dark side of — the

moon. _____   And it seems like it goes on like this for-ev - er,   you must for - give _____

me. _____   If I'm up and gone to Ca - ro - li - na in — my mind. _____

In my mind I'm gone to Ca - ro - li - na.   Can't you see the sun - shine?   And

can't you just see the moon - shine? — And ain't it just like a friend of mine — to hit me from — be-hind?

1.   — And I'm gone to Ca - ro - li - na in — my mind. —   2.   gone to Ca - ro - li - na

Repeat to Fade

in _____ my — mind. — _____   Gone to Ca - ro - li - na in — my mind.

13

Book 2

Sunny Skies

Words & Music by James Taylor

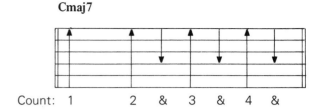

4/4 Rhythm Strumming/Swing
See Course Book No. 2 Page 5

Count: 1   2 & 3 & 4 &

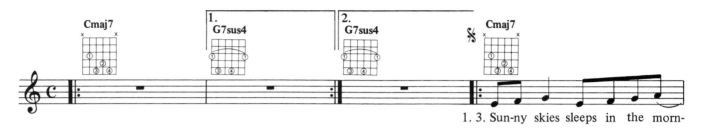

1. 3. Sun-ny skies sleeps in the morn-

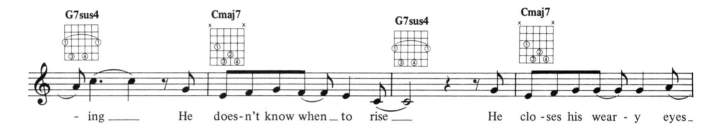

-ing ___ He does-n't know when ___ to rise ___ He clo-ses his wear-y eyes ___

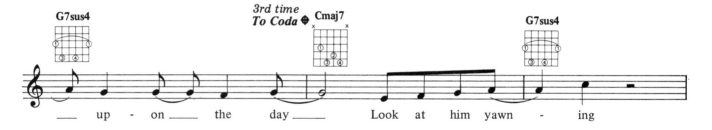

___ up - on ___ the day ___ Look at him yawn - ing

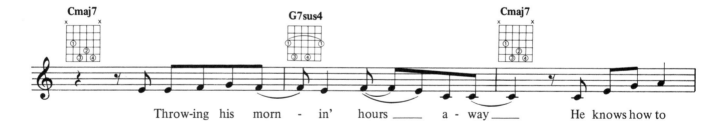

Throw-ing his morn - in' hours ___ a - way ___ He knows how to

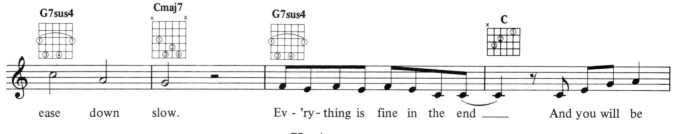

ease down slow. Ev - 'ry - thing is fine in the end ___ And you will be

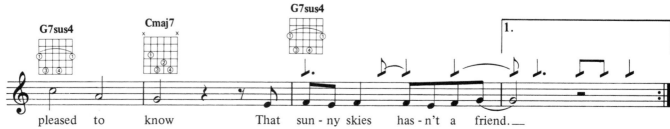

pleased to know That sun-ny skies has-n't a friend. ___

Verse 2
Sunny skies weeps in the evening
It doesn't much matter why
I guess he just has to cry from time to time
Everyone's leaving
And sunny skies has to stay behind.

Verse 3 on ‰. as Verse 1 to CODA

Hey Mister That's Me Up On The Jukebox
Words & Music by James Taylor

4/4 Rhythm Strumming
See Course Book No. 2 Page 10

CAPO 3rd FRET

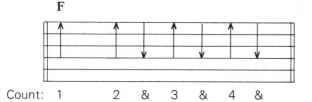

Count: 1   2 & 3 & 4 &

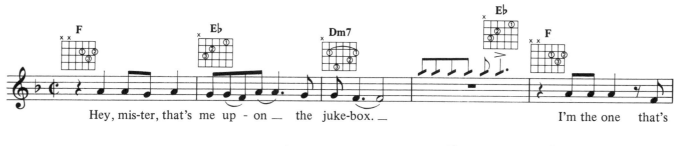

Hey, mis-ter, that's me up-on ___ the juke-box. ___   I'm the one that's

sing-in' this ___ sad song. ___   Well, I'll cry ev-'ry time   that you slip in one ___ more dime

___ and let the boy sing the sad ___ one one ___ more ___ time. ___   South-ern Ca-li-for-

- nia, that's as blue as the boy ___ can be. ___   Blue as the deep ___ blue sea, ___ won't you lis-ten to ___ me now.

___ I need your gold-en-gat-ed ci-ties ___ like a hole in the head;   just like a hole in the ___ head,

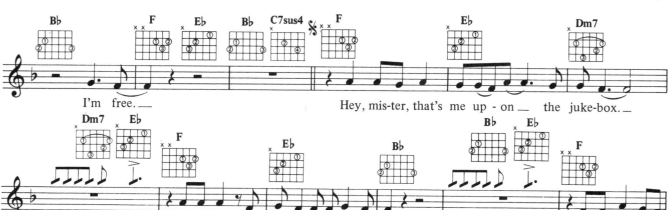

I'm free. ___   Hey, mis-ter, that's me up-on ___ the juke-box. ___

I'm the one that's sing-in' this ___ sad song. ___   Well I'll cry ev-'ry

time that you slip in one more dime and let the boy sing the sad one one more time.

I do be-lieve I'm head-ed home. Hey,

Mis-ter can't you see that I'm as dry as a bone. I think I'll spend some time a-

lone, yes, un-less you've found a way of squeez-in' wa-ter from a stone. Let the

doc-tor and the law-yer do as much as they can. Let the spring-time be-gin. Let the

boy be-come a man. I done wast-ed too much time just to sing you this sad song. I done

been this lone-some pick-er a lit-tle too long.

Well, I been spread-in' my-self thin these days, don't you know.

Good - bye.

Shower The People   Words & Music by James Taylor

Book 2

4/4 Rhythm/Arpeggio
See Course Book No. 2 Page 20

Count: 1 & 2 & 3 & 4 &

You can play the game__ and you can act out the part though you

know it was-n't writ-ten for you. ___ But tell me how can you stand there with your

bro-ken heart _____ a-shamed of play-ing the fool. ___

One thing can lead__ to an-oth-er; _____ it does-n't take an-y sac-ri-fice. ___ Oh,

fa-ther and mo-ther, sis-ter and bro-ther, if it feels nice ___ don't __ think twice.. Just

FULL RHYTHM STRUM

show-er the peo-ple you love ___ with love; ___ show them the way__ that you feel. __

___ Things are gon-na {work out / be just} fine, ___ if you on-ly will. __

18

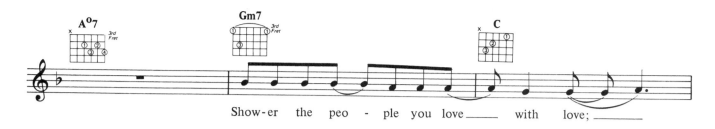

Show-er the peo - ple you love _____ with love; _____

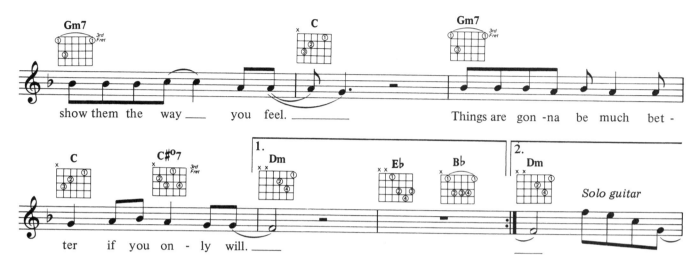

show them the way _____ you feel. _____ Things are gon -na be much bet -

ter if you on - ly will. _____

Solo guitar

Continue same guitar
figures from last 2 bars

Show-er the peo - ple you love _

Repeat and fade
(with vocal ad lib.)

_ with love; _____ show them the way _____ that you feel. _____

Verse 2
You can run but you cannot hide
This is widely known.
And what you plan to do with your pride,
When you're all by yourself alone
Once you tell somebody the way you feel
You can feel it beginning to ease
I think it's true what they say about the squeaky wheels
Always getting the grease. — Better —

Chorus
Shower the people . . . .

Vocal ad lib.
They say in every life,
They say the rain must fall.
Just like a pouring rain,
Make it rain.
Love is sunshine.

You Can Close Your Eyes Words & Music by James Taylor

4/4 Rhythm/Arpeggio
See Course Book No. 2 Page 20

Count: 1 & 2 & 3 & 4 &

Well, the sun is sure - ly sink - in' ___ down, but the moon is slow - ly ris - in'. ___ So this old world ___ must still ___ be spin - nin' 'round. And I still ___ love ___ you. ___ So close your ___ eyes. ___ You can close ___ your eyes, ___ it's all right. ___

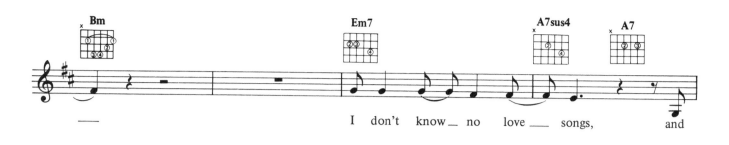

I don't know ___ no love ___ songs, ___ and

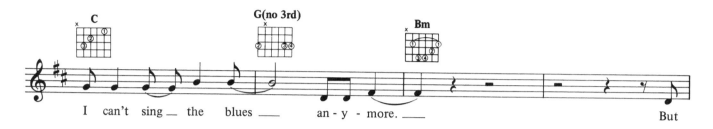

I can't sing ___ the blues ___ an - y - more. ___ But

I can sing ___ this song, ___ and you can sing ___ this song ___

___ when I'm gone.

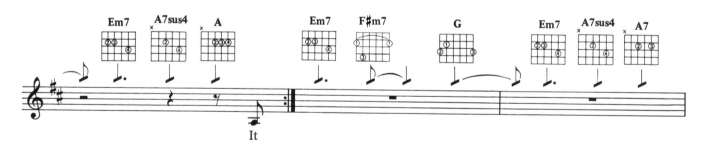

It

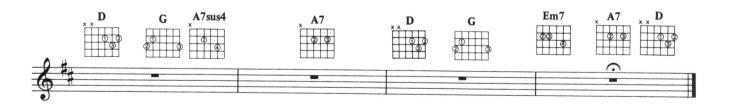

Verse 2
It won't be long before another day
We gonna have a good time
And no one's gonna take that tune away
You can stay as long as you like.

Riding On A Railroad

Words & Music by James Taylor

4/4 Rhythm/Alternating Thumb
See Course Book No. 2 Page 23

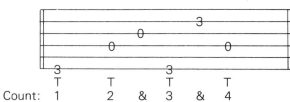

That's Why I'm Here

Words & Music by James Taylor

4/4 Rhythm/Alternating Thumb
See Course Book No. 2 Page 23

CAPO 3rd FRET

Per - son to per - son and man ___ to man, ___ I'm back in touch with my long ___

___ lost friend. Lis-ten to rea - son and un - der-stand and think of my from way back when.

He said, "Me and Me-lis - sa, well we fell out of love.___ We ran out of luck, seems like

light - ning struck. I've been think-in' of leav - in' but I can't raise a buck.___ James, I'm

CHORUS

won-drin', could I bor - row your truck?" I said: That's why I'm here.

(That's why I'm

Got no bet-ter rea-son. That's why I'm stand - in' be-fore ya.

here. ___) (That's why I'm

To Coda ✛

1.

2.

That's why I'm here.

here. ___) John's

This is an I. O. U. Reck-on I owe you one now.

Lis-ten, Wen-dy; lis-ten, Glo-ria. This-'ll be bet-ter to-mor-row. Oh,

CODA

This is the part a-bout Cook-ie and Bill.— He loved her— and she— loved him.—

Wake him up, shake him up in the mid-dle of the night. Got to tell me ev-'ry-thing's al-right.—

— I said: That's why I'm ——— here. Got me walk-in' and— talk-in' like a
(That's why I'm here. ———)

nat-'ral man. That's why I'm here. That's why I'm — here.—
(That's why I'm here. ———)

That's right.

Verse 2:
John's gone, found dead. He dies high, he's brown bread
Later said to have drowned in his bed.
After the laughter, the wave of dread
It hits us like a ton of lead
It seems they're not to burn means they turn on a dime
And walk on if you're walking even if it's an uphill climb
Try to remember that working's no crime
Just don't let them take your wasted time.

Chorus
That's why I'm here
There'll be more message tonight
That's why I'm here
That's why I'm here.

Verse 3 (on S.)
Oh, fortune and fame, such a curious game
Perfect strangers can call you by name
And pay good money to hear "Fire and Rain"
Again and again and again.
Oh, some are like summer, comin' back every year
Got your baby, got your blanket, got your bucket of beer.
I break into a grin from ear to ear
And suddenly it's perfectly clear.

Chorus
That's why I'm here
Singing tonight, tomorrow and everyday.
That's why I'm standin'.
That's why I'm here.

Handy Man

Words & Music by Otis Blackwell & Jimmy Jones

4/4 Rhythm/Alternating Thumb
See Course Book No. 2 Page 25

Highway Song

Words & Music by James Taylor

4/4 Rhythm/Strumming
See Course Book No. 3 Page 6

Count: 1   2 & 3 & 4 &

Fa-ther,   let us build a boat and sail a-way. There's noth-in' for you here.

And bro-ther, let us throw our lot out up-on the sea.

It's been done be-fore. I'm think-in' 'bout a bro-ken heart. I'm

talk-in' 'bout the break of dawn. You me while I'm here. Then you can miss

me when I'm gone. Sweet mis-un-der-stand-in', won't you

leave a poor boy a-lone? I'm the one-eyed seed of a tum-ble-weed in the

bel-ly of a roll-in' stone. Back on the high-way, yeah, yeah, yeah.

To Coda ⊕

1.

Back on the road a-gain. Now

Now one of these days that high-way song will lose its ap-peal to me. I'm gon-na

set-tle on down like a nat-'ral born man. I'm gon-na live my life nat-'ral-ly. (Free and ea-sy.) Un-

til that day the thun-der's gon-na roll, and I no-tice there's a sign of rain. So I grab

my bags and I pack my clothes and I'm back on the road a-gain. Back on the

high-way, yeah, yeah, yeah. Back on the road a-gain.

D.%. al Coda   CODA

I'm   Here I am a-gain, Ho-li-day Inn.

Same old four walls a-gain. Gee, but it's fine to be back home a-gain, whoa, now.

Say, Ho-li-day Inn, I'm on the road a-gain.

Verse 2
(Now) had a little woman in Memphis,
She wanted to be my bride
She said, 'Settle on down, travelin' man
You can stay right by my side.'
I tried so hard to please her
But I couldn't hold out too long
'Cause one Saturday night I was layin' in bed,
And I heard that highway song.

Verse 3 (on %.)
I'm thinkin' about a broken heart
I been talkin' 'bout the break of dawn
You loved me while I'm here
And you can miss me when I'm gone
Sweet misunderstandin'
Won't you leave a poor boy alone?
'Cause I'm the one eyed seed of a tumbleweed
In the belly of a rollin' stone.

Mud Slide Slim
Words & Music by James Taylor

4/4 Rhythm/Syncopated Arpeggio
See Course Book No. 3 Page 20

CAPO 3rd FRET

Verse 2 (on S.)
(I'm gonna) cash in my hand and pick up a piece of land
And build myself a cabin back in the woods.
Lord it's there I'm gonna stay until there comes a day
When this old world starts changing for the good
Now the reason I'm smiling is over an island
On a hillside in the woods where I belong.
I wanna thank Jimmy, Jimmy, John and Nick and Laurie
The No Jets construction for setting me down a homestead on the farm.

Fire And Rain

Words & Music by James Taylor

4/4 Rhythm Arpeggio/Alternating thumb
See Course Book No. 3 Page 23

CAPO 3rd FRET

VERSES 1 & 2

Just yes-ter-day morn-ing ___ they let me know ___ you were gone ___

Su-san, the plans they made put an end to you   I walked out this morn-ing   and I

wrote down this song ___   I just can't re-mem-ber who to send ___

CHORUS

___ it to. ___   I've seen fire and I seen rain   I've seen

sun-ny days ___ that I thought ___ would ne-ver end ___   I've seen

Verse 2
Look down upon me Jesus, you gotta help me make a stand
You've just gotta see me through another day.
My body's aching, and my time is at hand
And I won't make it any other way.

Gorilla Words & Music by James Taylor

4/4 Rhythm/Bass Strum/Swing
See Course Book No. 3 Page 11

Count: 1 2 & 3 & 4 &

He's got arms like legs, he's got hands on his feet. He's got a nose like a dough-nut, he's got a ten-den-cy to o-ver-eat. He don't use tools or wea-pons, he don't eat meat. He likes to stick to the bush-es, tends to a-void the street. But he rides my El Do-ra-do, ba-by, when he comes to town. You know he's out there some-where try'n' to track you down.

1, 2. *3.* He's still a go-ril-la.

Verse 2: Look up in the sky, mama that's the one.
See the mighty profile, block the noon day sun.
He comes from the heart of darkness, a thousand miles from here.
That's the land where they understand — what a woman might like to hear.
You know that he loves you, baby, for what you really are.
His love is as burning hot as a big old ten cent cigar.

Verse 3: Now most of y'all have seen, a gorilla in a cage at the local zoo.
He mostly sits around contemplating all the things that he'd prefer to do.
He dreams about the world outside from behind those bars of steel.
And no one seems to understand about the heartache the man can feel.
The people stop and stare, but nobody seems to care.
It don't seem right somehow, it just don't seem fair.

Suite For 20G
Words & Music by James Taylor

4/4 Rhythm/Syncopated Arpeggio
See Course Book No. 4 Page 23

CAPO 1st FRET

Accompaniment picking for VERSE

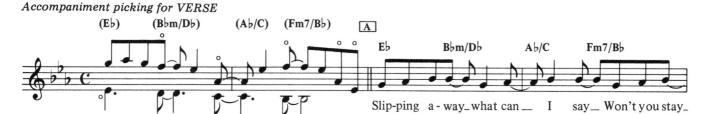

Slip-ping a-way_ what can _ I say_ Won't you stay_

_ in - side _ my month _ of May_ And hold on to _ me gold - en day,_ slip-ping a-way._

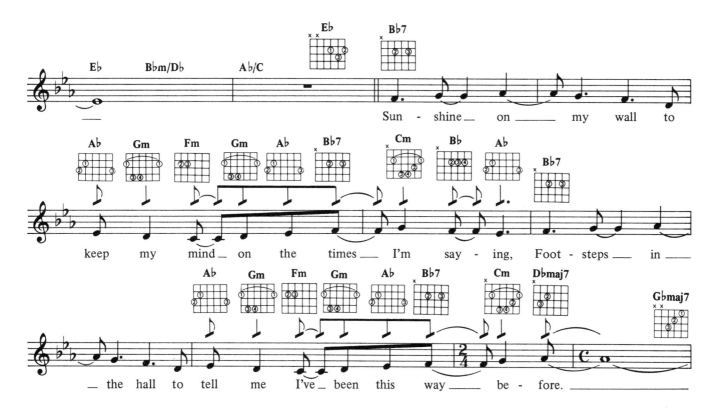

_ Sun - shine_ on _ my wall to keep my mind_ on the times _ I'm say - ing, Foot - steps _ in _

_ the hall to tell me I've _ been this way _ be - fore. _

Accompaniment pattern

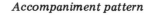

_ Let it rain, _ Sweet Ma - ry Jane, Let it wash _ your love down all _ a - round _ me,

Come in - side _ and put _ it down _ let it rain. _

e - nough to eat, now, Hold my soul __ I sure __ am fond __ of my rock

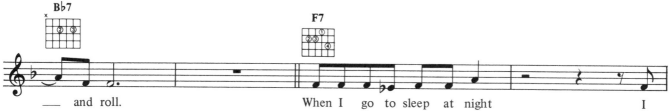

__ and roll. When I go to sleep at night I

want to hear a slide gui-tar _____ When I'm feel-in' loose and right

Rid-in' in my au-to-mo-bile __ Bo-ney Ma-ro - ney and __ Peg-gy Sue

Rock-ing pneu-mo-nia, got the Boo - gie Woo-gie flu __ Hold my soul __

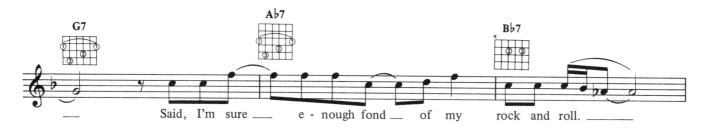

__ Said, I'm sure __ e - nough fond __ of my rock and roll. __

Repeat to Fade

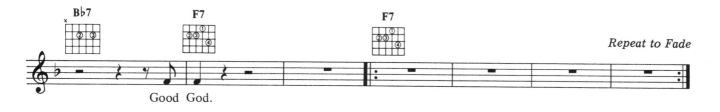

Good God.

Repeat at B
This time 'round I'm searching down to where I used to go
And it's been on my mind to make it shine.

37

Brighten Your Night With My Day

Words & Music by James Taylor

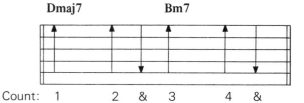

4/4 Rhythm/Strumming
See Course Book No. 4 Page 7

Day-break ___ finds you up and a-live ___ just as though you could

touch a star; ___ But sun-set ___ seems to leave you wear-y a-lone and won-der-ing

who you are. ___ Don't de-ny that lone-ly feel-ing that

keeps steal-ing on you from deep down in-side; ___ Hey can't you see that it's

no good con-ceal-ing a feel-ing it hurts ___ you to hide ___ When you can come

home to me. ___ Yes, I'm hap-py to hear ___ what you've got to say to me, babe, all the

Long Ago and Far Away

Words & Music by James Taylor

4/4 Rhythm/Mixed Arpeggio
See Course Book No. 4 Page 14

CAPO 2nd FRET

Count: 1 & 2 & 3 & 4 &

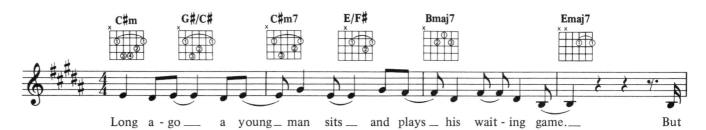

Long a - go ___ a young ___ man sits ___ and plays ___ his wait - ing game. ___ But

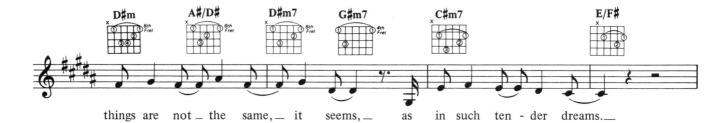

things are not ___ the same, ___ it seems, ___ as in such ten - der dreams. ___

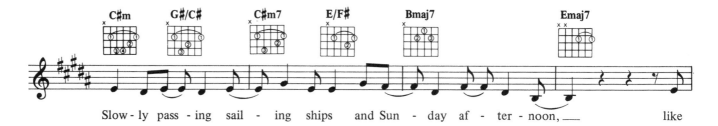

Slow - ly pass - ing sail - ing ships and Sun - day af - ter - noon, ___ like

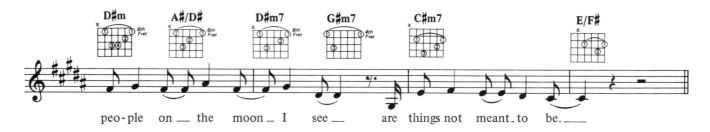

peo - ple on ___ the moon ___ I see ___ are things not meant ___ to be. ___

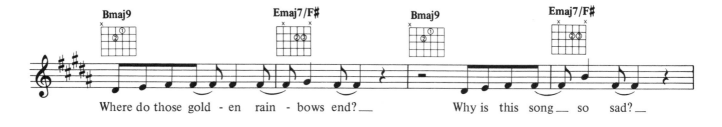

Where do those gold - en rain - bows end? ___ Why is this song ___ so sad? ___

Dream - ing the dreams I've dreamed, my friend, ___ lov - ing the love ___ I love ___ to love ___

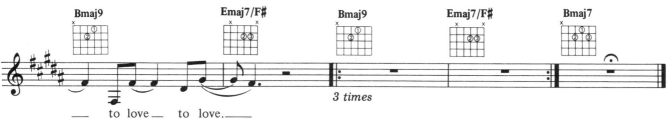

Lo And Behold

Words & Music by James Taylor

4/4 Rhythm/Arpeggio and
embellishments with 3rds and 6ths
See Course Book No. 4 Pages 16-22

CAPO 3rd FRET

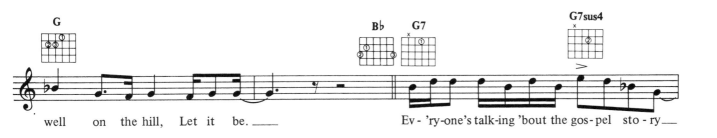

well　　on the hill,　Let it be. ___　　　　　　Ev - 'ry-one's talk-ing 'bout the gos-pel sto - ry ___

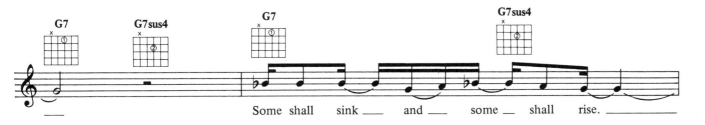

___　　　　　　　　Some shall　sink ___ and ___ some ___ shall　rise. ___

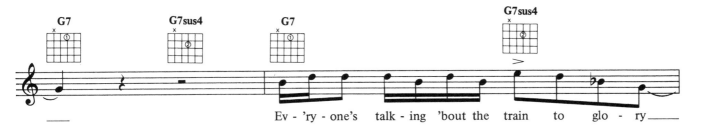

___　　　　　　　　Ev - 'ry - one's　talk - ing 'bout the　train　to　glo - ry ___

___　　　　　　　　Long,　long　time till　it　gets ___ here to you ba - by. ___

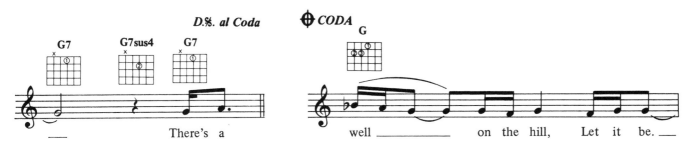

D.%. al Coda　　　⊕ *CODA*

___　　　　　There's a　　　well ___ on the hill,　Let it be. ___

Country Road

Words & Music by James Taylor

4/4 Rhythm/Alternating thumb in
D tuning with embellishments
See Course Book No. 4 Pages 16-22

TUNE LOWER STRING TO D

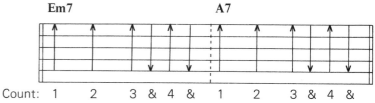

Count: 1   2   3 & 4 &   1   2   3 & 4 &

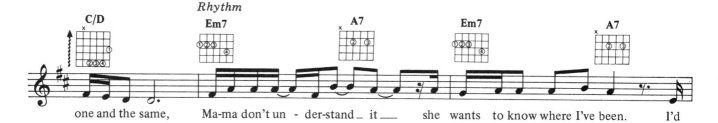

Take — to the high-way won't you lend me — your name — Your way — and my way seem to be

one and the same, Ma-ma don't un-der-stand — it — she wants to know where I've been.   I'd

have to be some — kind of nat-ural born fool to want to pass that way a-gain — But you know I could
(2nd time) But I could be

As Intro 4 bars solo guitar

To Coda ⊕

feel it. —   On a coun-try road. —

I guess my feet — know where they want me to go _____   walk-ing on a coun-try road.

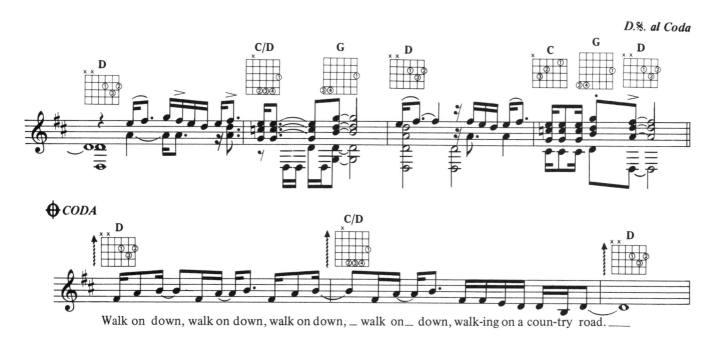

Walk on down, walk on down, walk on down, __ walk on __ down, walk-ing on a coun-try road. ____

La la   la la __ la la la la   la la __ la la ____   la la la la   la la   la la la __ la la __ la la ____ Coun-try road

Similar to Intro figures   *Repeat and Fade*

____   ____   Walk-ing   on a coun-try road. ____   Coun-try road

Verse 2
Sail on to Jesus won't you good girls and boys?
I'm all in pieces you can have your own choice
But I can see a heavenly band
Full of angels coming to set me free
I don't know nothing 'bout the why or when,
But I can tell you that it's bound to be —
Because I could feel it.

You've Got A Friend
Words & Music by Carole King

4/4 Rhythm/Syncopated Arpeggio and alternating thumb mix
See Course Book No. 4 Page 23

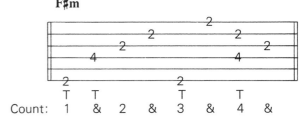

Verse 2
If the sky, above you, should turn dark and full of clouds
And that old north wind should begin to blow
Keep your head together, and call my name out loud
And soon, you'll hear me knocking upon your door.

Oh Susanna Traditional. Arranged by James Taylor

4/4 Rhythm/Arpeggios & Embellishments
See Course Book No. 4 Pages 16-22

CAPO 3rd FRET

Verse 2
Well I had myself a dream the other night
When everything was still
I dreamed I saw my girl Suzanne
She was coming around the hill.
The buckwheat cake was in her mouth
The tear was in her eye
I said that I come from Dixieland
Suzanne don't you break down and cry

Chorus [as 1st Chorus]